Disney
FROZEN II
500 Stickers

AUTUMN PUBLISHING

Story Time

Young Anna and Elsa love listening to their parents' tales about the past.
Spot six differences between the two pictures below.

a

b

Answers at the back of the book

Sister Match

Only one of the small pictures of Elsa below matches the larger picture. Which one is it?

Which small picture below matches the big picture of Anna?

Answers at the back of the book

Memory Game

Look at the picture below for 30 seconds, then cover it up
and answer the questions at the bottom of the page.

a) How many trolls are there?

b) What colour dress is Anna wearing?

c) Is Olaf in the picture?

d) Are the trolls wearing necklaces?

Answers at the back of the book

Elements Sudoku

Use the key to choose the correct picture in the grid.
Each column and row should contain all four elements.

Friends Close-Up

Which close-up at the bottom of the page isn't part of the picture?

a

b

c

d

e

Answers at the back of the book

Forest Maze

Anna, Elsa and their friends need help finding their way through the Enchanted Forest. Guide them through the maze.

START

FINISH

Answers at the back of the book

Sliding Snowman

Using the grid as a guide, draw this picture of Olaf by copying the squares one by one. Then, colour him in!

True Shadows

Only one of these shadows belongs to Anna. Which one is it?

a

b

c

d

Arendellian Doodle

Draw a design on Mattias's shield.

In My Element

Complete the patterns below by figuring out which element comes next in the sequence. Draw the correct picture in the box.

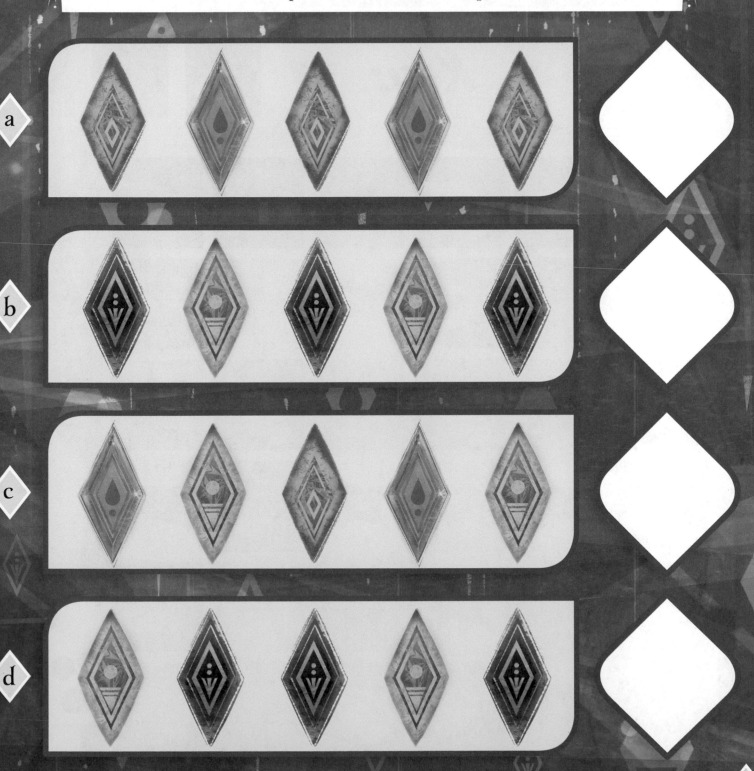

Nature's Path

Use the key to help you find the
correct route through the leaves.

Key:

Start

Flaming Fun!

Connect the dots to reveal the Fire Spirit.

Friends Mix-Up

This picture of the Arendelle friends is jumbled up. Label the pieces in the correct order below.

Answers

a	b	c	d	e	f	g	h
○	○	○	○	○	○	○	○

Answers at the back of the book

Hidden Forest

Can you find the word FOREST
hidden in the wordsearch five times?

F	I	F	G	N	P	C	F
S	O	O	M	A	P	J	O
F	O	R	E	S	T	I	R
B	B	E	E	K	X	Y	E
M	P	S	D	S	D	C	S
K	H	T	R	V	T	U	T
S	F	O	R	E	S	T	P
L	J	A	Z	Q	O	C	I

Answers at the back of the book

Doodle Magic

Can you create your own mystical forest, with trees,
leaves and animals? Doodle your ideas above.

Kristoff Differences

One picture of Kristoff is different to the others.
Look closely to see if you can spot which one it is.

a   b   c   d

Name Game

Unscramble the letters to reveal
the name of Sven's closest friend.

F K S O R I F T

Answers at the back of the book

Mythical Path

Anna and Elsa have become separated from Olaf. Which path will lead them to him?

a   b   c

Answers at the back of the book

Fearless Family

Anna and Elsa face their destiny together. Can you find six differences between the two pictures of them?

a

b

Earth Shaker!

Connect the dots to reveal the ground-shaking creature.

Copy Colours

Use your best pencils to colour in the Fire Spirit,
using the small picture to help you.

Deep Water

Complete the picture of Elsa and the Water Nokk
by working out where the jigsaw pieces belong.

Answers at the back of the book

Use the decoder to reveal the mystery word.

A	B	C	D	E	F	G	H	I	J	K	L	M
N	O	P	Q	R	S	T	U	V	W	X	Y	Z

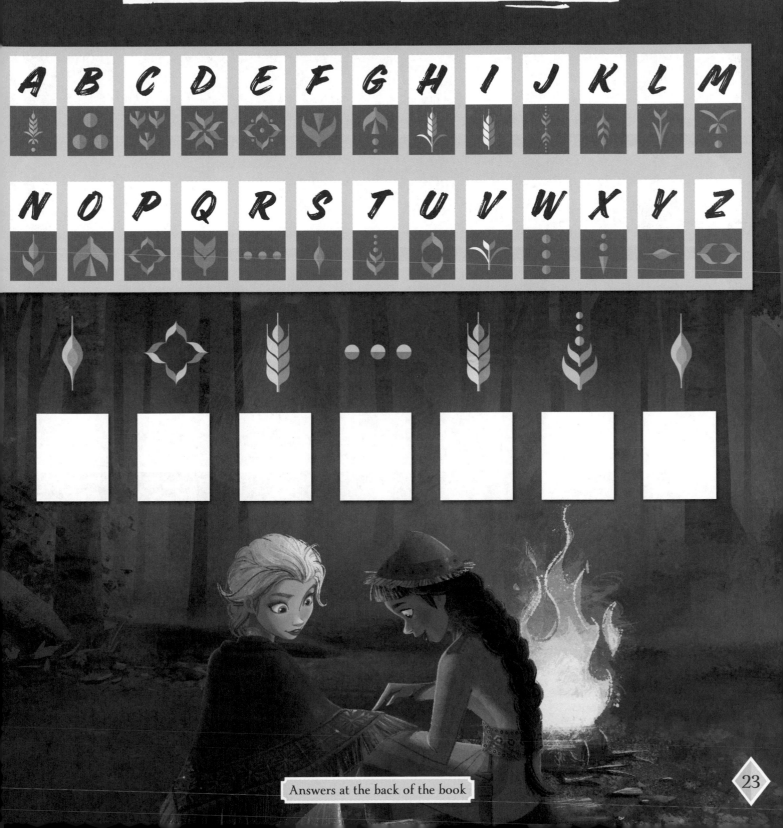

Snowy Patterns

Olaf has learned lots of new things! Help him complete the patterns below by writing the correct numbers in the boxes.

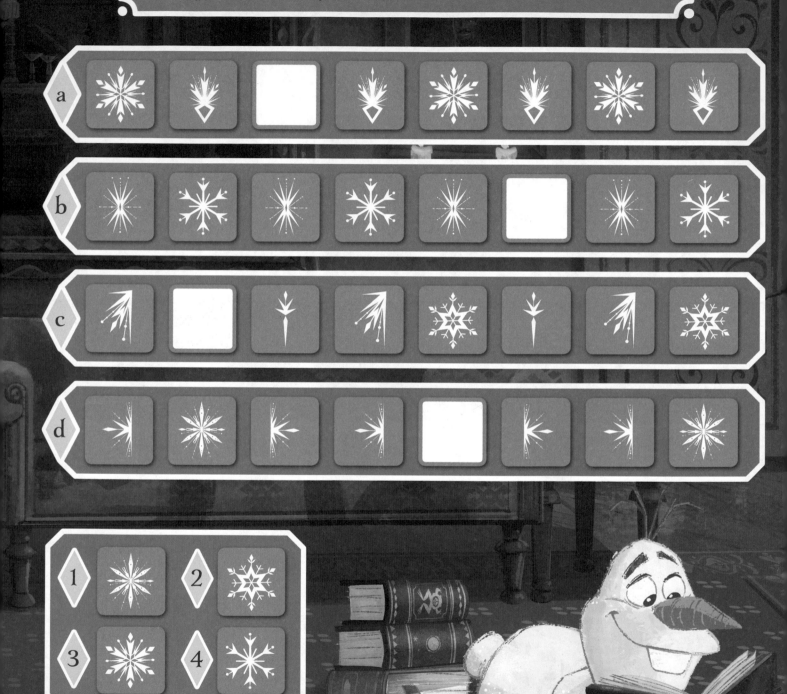

Answers at the back of the book

Giant Jigsaw

Anna and Olaf don't want to wake the Earth Giants.
Draw lines to where the jigsaw pieces belong to complete the picture.

1

2

3

4

5

Answers at the back of the book

Olaf Shadow

Which shadow belongs to the lovable snowman?

Answers at the back of the book

Perfect Pair

Only one of the smaller pictures of Anna and Elsa matches the bigger picture. Which one is it?

Answers at the back of the book

Ice Breaker

Using the key at the bottom of the page, help Anna and Olaf break the icy code to reveal an important message.

Mythical Puzzle

Complete the puzzle below by making sure each row, column and box contains only one character. Write your answers in the spaces.

Hidden Truth

Anna and Olaf need to find their way through the cave.
Complete the maze to help them.

START

FINISH

ANSWERS

Page 2

Page 3
Elsa - b; Anna - a

Page 4
a – 9, b – Green, c – No, d – Yes

Page 5
1 – a, 2 – c, 3 – d, 4 – b

Page 6
Close-up d is not part of the picture

Page 7

Page 9
Shadow c belongs to Anna

Page 11
a   b   c   d

Page 12

Start

Finish

Page 14
a – 1 b – 5, c – 2, d – 7,
e – 6, f – 4, g – 3, h – 8

Page 15

F	I	F	G	N	P	C	F
S	O	O	M	A	P	J	O
F	O	R	E	S	T	I	R
B	B	E	E	K	X	Y	E
M	P	S	D	S	D	C	S
K	H	T	R	V	U	U	T
S	F	O	R	E	S	T	P
L	J	A	Z	Q	O	C	I

Page 17
Picture d is different to the others

ANSWERS

Page 17
KRISTOFF

Page 18
Path c will lead to Olaf

Page 19

Page 22
a - 4, b - 3, c - 5, d - 1, e - 2

Page 23
SPIRITS

Page 24
a - 3, b - 4, c -2, d - 1

Page 25
a - 5, b - 2, c - 4, d - 1, e - 3

Page 26
Shadow d belongs to Olaf

Page 27
Picture c matches the bigger picture

Page 28
DO THE NEXT RIGHT THING

Page 29
a – 6, b – 2, c – 1, d – 8,
e – 3, f – 5, g – 9, h – 4, i – 7

Page 30

Disney
FROZEN II
500
Stickers

Join Anna and Elsa for a
sticker and activity adventure!

With 500 awesome stickers and
lots of activities and puzzles, this
book is perfect for Frozen
fans everywhere.

For more exciting
Disney
books, visit
igloobooks.com

Published in 2019
by Autumn Publishing
Cottage Farm, NN6 0BJ

Autumn is an imprint of Bonnier Books UK

© 2019 Disney Enterprises, Inc.
All rights reserved.

1119 001

10 9 8 7 6 5 4 3 2 1

ISBN 978-1-83852-740-2

Printed and manufactured in China

UK   £3.99   CE   * ISBN 978-1-8385

AUTUMN
PUBLISHING
visit us at - www.igloobooks.com

9 781838 527402

KS-905-610

© Disney

© Disney